WINDSOR HASSLE

WINDSOR HASSLE

Paul K. Willis

Illustrated by Ted Michener

CBC Enterprises

MONTRÉAL • TORONTO • NEW YORK • LONDON

Published by CBC Enterprises/Les Entreprises Radio-Canada, a division of the Canadian
Broadcasting Corporation, P.O. Box 500, Station A, Toronto (Ontario), Canada
M5W 1E6

Canadian Cataloguing in Publication Data
Willis, Paul K. 1947–
  Windsor hassle

ISBN 0-88794-325-X

1. Windsor, House of – Anecdotes, facetiae, satire, etc.
2. Windsor, House of – Fiction. I. CBC Enterprises.
II. Title.

PS8595.W55W5 1987   C818'.5407   C87-094412-6
PR9199.3.W55W5 1987

Editor: Beverley Beetham Endersby
Design: Peter Maher
Typesetter: Crocker Bryant Inc.

Distributed to the trade by
McClelland and Stewart, Toronto.

Printed and bound in Canada by John Deyell Company
1 2 3 4 5 6 / 92 91 90 89 88 87

TO
John Disney,
executive producer, "Basic Black,"
who said, "Maybe it should be a soap opera."

Yet Another Endorsement by

Princess Michael of Kent

Although I have not read *Windsor Hassle* I heartily recommend it to all and sundry. When the publishers first contacted me I was staying with Phillipa Wigmore (do you know her?) in St. Moritz and, after spirited trans-Atlantic negotiations, I agreed (anything to stop those incessant phone calls) to write these few words for a paltry fee (you'd only laugh, my dear).

By sheer coincidence I shall be travelling to your country in the very near future where I shall be engaged in public-relations work for one of your leading purveyors of convenience foods (It's a good time for the great taste of McDonald's). I look forward to meeting many of you as I travel through the provinces of British Columbia, Alberta, and Saskatoon.

Windsor Hassle is a very fine book with many excellent words and lovely pictures.

Yours in haste,

Michael

01-555-9720
(After 5:00) 01-555-9721

FOREWORD

I have never been inside Windsor Castle but I have been inside Buckingham Palace. It is therefore fitting that I, a person who has supped with the best of 'em, should have been asked to write a foreword to this book. I quickly add that supping with the best of 'em did not include a dinner with you-know-who and the family. My visit consisted of a quick skid through the corridors of power and out through the kitchen before the guards changed for the daily visitors. Unfortunately the Queen was off frolicking in an ex colony, convincing them that although they were no longer part of the mother country, mother herself had indeed not forgotten them.

So it was with absolute delight that I switched on my radio one Saturday morning to find that the very person I'd hoped to meet had been captured in a weekly series, fritting around the pans and dishes as easily as you and me.

What joy, what bliss, to find that her life and that of the family was little different from my own.

What was wonderful listening on a Saturday morning has now become wonderful reading any day of the week. So down with the drawbridge and open wide the gates, we're coming through.

Hold on, I was first…Will you stop pushing!…Take your elbows out of my back!…

Ben Wicks
TORONTO

IElizabeth the Second, by the grace of God, of the United Kingdom of Great Britain and Northern Ireland, head of the Commonwealth, Defender of the Faith…am not home right now. But if you will leave a message We shall get back to you."

In fact the Queen *was* home. She was watching "Dallas." She was not amused. A puzzling note from the Foreign Office had left her vaguely disquieted and, besides, she considered Bobby's return from the dead to have been handled badly, highly improbable.

And then there was this vexing business of Philip. He was out again giving a talk, this time to the Royal Geographical Society. All week he had been very secretive, refusing to reveal the topic. The Queen feared the worst.

In the Barbican Centre conference room the smoke was rising and the brandy was flowing as the Duke swung into his conclusion.

"And so, gentlemen, I would urge you not to think of the Chinese as a mass of slitty-eyed foreign devils" — here he paused for effect — "but rather as our little yellow friends."

The ensuing uproar left the Duke well satisfied.

Princess Margaret Rose peered out the windows of number 1-A Clock Court, Kensington Palace, towards the gardens below. The brilliance of afternoon had faded now to an anaemic pink that dusted the trees and played across the great expanse of emerald green. Margaret inhaled deeply. *Oh my, she thought, this really is excellent hashish.*

Her fingers idly brushed the keys of the piano, a gift of the people of Zambia. So what would it be this evening?

Chopin? A little Debussy? She thought a moment. Then a melody echoed down the passageways and through the thirty-five rooms that Margaret Rose had come to detest.

My baby takes the morning train,
He works from nine to five and then…

And then suddenly it was 1964. It was another piano and Dudley Moore at the Elephant Club. He was playing for Margaret. They had all played for Margaret then. Was it really so very long ago?

There were new princesses now. The editorial assistant and the kindergarten teacher…no-better-than-they-ought-to-be's. They'd pushed Margaret out of the spotlight, reduced her to aunthood.

Slowly Margaret became aware that she was pounding her fists into the keyboard. A last crescendo reverberated through the halls.

T he Queen was in the parlour eating bread and honey. It was "by appointment."

"Anything interesting in the morning post?" asked Philip.

"Not really," said the Queen. "Oh…here's something."

"Mmmmm? What's that?" Philip had been enjoying the lead story in the *Sun*: "Duke Racist Rabble Rouser!" He waited while the Queen scanned the note.

"Death threat."

"Oh?"

"It's for you." She slid the note across the table and had a go at the next envelope. "Oh dear."

Philip looked up again. "What's that?"

"The Canadians want us."

"Bloody hell!" said Philip. He didn't much care for Canadians.

"It's from Mayor Ralph Klein of Calgary. Wants us to

open something called Yahoo Days."

Philip struggled to place the name. "He's the one who smokes marijuana."

"No dear," the Queen explained patiently, "you know that's Mr. Hatfield."

"Well," said Philip, "tell him to bugger off."

"Yes, I may have to. I think we're in Yemen that week." Philip went back to his reading. "Of course," said the Queen a moment later, "we could always send Charles and Diana." Philip lowered the paper. His face brightened.

"Yes," he said, "we could at that. Serve them bloody well right too."

"Charles said they'd be dropping by this afternoon. I'll bring it up with them then. Now that's odd." The Queen had opened another envelope.

"What's up?" asked Philip.

"It's from the Prime Minister. She wants to see me this afternoon."

"The grocer's daughter? She's not due till Tuesday."

"Yes, I know," said the Queen. "But she says it's a matter of some urgency."

"Probably wants to bomb someone," Philip mumbled. He'd given up trying to read. The Queen peered at him over her glasses.

"Not if I have anything to say about it," she said. "By the way, what have you got on today?"

"Oh, nothing much. Luncheon with the Sultan of Oman, then I thought I'd chew out Edward for a while."

"How nice," said the Queen. "It does my heart good to see you two spending time together."

T he world's-most-powerful-woman's Bentley slowed as it entered a side gate of Buckingham Palace. Its sole occupant studied the reflection of her own face in the window. *Beloved by millions, the mother of her nation, the single great unifying presence in a commonwealth of nations*...Margaret Thatcher knew these things to be untrue but she found it helped if she repeated them over and over to herself. Meeting with the Queen could be unnerving. Now the car was slowing to a stop.

"Your Majesty, thank you for seeing me on such short notice." Margaret thought the Queen looked pale and drawn. "And may I say how very well you look today?"

"Yes you may. Sit down." *So, she's going to be like that*, the Prime Minister thought. "You said you had to see me about an urgent matter?"

"Yes, Your Majesty. I must tell you that it is a matter requiring enormous discretion."

"Yes, yes, Prime Minister, do get on with it." The Queen hated it when Margaret Thatcher went all "Falkland Islands" on her.

The Queen watched as the Prime Minister fished into her gigantic handbag.

For one dreadful moment Margaret Thatcher thought she had forgotten to bring it. But, ah, there it was — a manila envelope nestling against the canister of Mace. "This morning, Your Majesty, MI-5 intercepted this." She laid the envelope on the table.

"Oh?"

The Prime Minister noted with satisfaction the glint of interest in the Queen's eye. "It contains certain photographs."

"Photographs?"

"Yes, Your Majesty. Photographs of a man and a woman. I am sorry to have to tell you that they are obscene in nature."

"No need to be sorry, Prime Minister," said the Queen, "unless of course you yourself are depicted."

"Certainly not," replied the Prime Minister, "although" — and here she feared her voice might betray some secret pleasure — "I believe you are acquainted with at least one of the participants."

"We'd better have a look then." Margaret watched as the Queen reached for the envelope. She timed her next words carefully.

"MI-5 informs me that a certain newspaper publisher already has these self-same photographs in his possession." For a long moment the Queen examined them.

"Well, Your Majesty?"

"Well," said the Queen, "it's not a very good likeness of Andrew."

D iana," said the Queen. There was no response. The consort to the future forty-third monarch lounged with a beatific smile upon her face. Confident, aware, impeccably turned out — a woman for the 'eighties.

"Charles," said the Queen, "kindly remove those earphones from Diana's head."

"Oh, was someone saying something?" Diana tossed her hair.

"It's Mama," said Charles. "She wants to talk to us."

"What about?" Diana was anxious to get back to the Blow Monkeys.

"It's this," said the Queen, raising the Hallmark card as a visual aid, "an invitation from Canada. I want you two to go."

"Canada?" cried Charles, "not again!" Diana sprang to her feet.

"Canada. Absolutely not. I'd rather be dead!"

"But, Mama, we were just there," Charles protested, "at that Expo thing. It was so boring Diana had to pretend to faint."

Diana had begun to pace about.

"Charles is right. It was horrid! I'm sure I can't do it again."

"There's no good in you two going on like this." The Queen had expected just such an outburst. "You'll go to Canada or I'll know the reason why not."

Diana stopped her pacing. "I think I have a reason," she said.

"Oh?" said the Queen. "It had better be a good one."

Diana ducked her head and began to pluck demurely at her ruching.

"It's because... I'm expecting."

Charles was the first to react. "Expecting what?"

"A baby, you twit."

"I see," said the Queen.

Somewhere a clock was ticking.

Once before Philip had felt this way — during the war when he'd been ordered to interrogate an Italian POW. He remembered his rage at the man's stupid responses to his keen, intelligent questions. Now he felt that rage again.

"You idiot!" he thundered. "You're determined to make a laughing stock of us all! First the marines and now this!"

"Please, Papa," cried Edward, "it's too hard! The other boys laugh at me and call me names!"

"No gumption, that's your problem!" Philip bellowed. He could be heard entire floors away. Members of the staff froze in their tracks.

Edward was now in tears. "Please, Papa, let me quit! I can't bear it any longer!"

"Quit?" raged the Duke. "I think not, my boy! You'll stick it out! It was your idea to take jazz-tap lessons and you'll bloody well continue to take jazz-tap lessons! And that's my final word!"

"… mindful of the Church's teaching that Christian marriage is indissoluble, and conscious of my duty to the Commonwealth … I have decided not to marry Group Captain Peter Townsend." The paper had yellowed, but Margaret Rose had kept it all these years in a little box, with the others. She pulled out another.

"… have regretfully concluded that she, and The Right Honourable the Earl of Snowdon will amicably separate until such time as a formal dissolution of their marriage …" The newspaper clipping had faded, but Margaret had kept it all these years. Ah, and what was this?

"Snuggles: Just popped out for a pack of cigs. Love ya, Roddy." The handwriting seemed childish now, but Margaret had kept it too. All these years. In a little box.

Curious how one's life came down to a few scraps of paper. Curious how one felt the need to treasure them. Curious how the flames turned each into a thin film of carbon as one dropped them one by one into the big onyx ashtray, a gift of the people of Peru.

The Aston Martin had the capability of achieving a speed of one hundred and twenty kilometres per hour in under thirty seconds. Charles was doing forty.

"Diana," he was saying, "I must say I'm flabbergasted. Why didn't you tell me you were pregnant?"

Diana had been staring out the window. Now she turned. "Because I'm not," she said.

"What? I don't understand."

Diana sighed. "Charles, you have to have sex to get pregnant."

Charles considered the logic of this for a moment.

"Yes, I suppose that's true. But why would you make up a story like that? Mama's sure to find out."

"Of course she is. That's why you damn well better make

sure I am pregnant, and soon."

"Right," said Charles. "See what you mean. Better get to it then."

The Aston Martin's speedometer registered forty-five.

Andrew spotted the Argentinians before they saw him; a large group clustered in front of a low building. Obviously some sort of barracks.

"Never mind, Eggerton, I'll take it from here," he said, seizing the controls. He swung the Lynx around, putting his back to the sun. The element of surprise. Now he was in a steep dive. Andrew felt the exhilaration of battle and savoured the blood pounding in his temples. "Stand by to fire the AS-12's!"

"Sir?" asked Eggerton.

"Don't question my orders, man! Fire the damned things!"

The Oldenbrook Seniors' Fellowship Home had been built by public subscription. The need had been great. In its grim industrial setting it stood out as a beacon of hope to the aged yearning to spend their twilight years in some modicum of comfort. News that Prince Andrew would officiate at the opening ceremonies had spread quickly and by ten o'clock a considerable crowd of the elderly had gathered.

At first sight of the Prince's helicopter a ragged cheer had gone up. Then, for a moment the helicopter disappeared, lost in the sun.

"Fire the damn things!" Andrew ordered, a second time.

"No, sir, I won't!"

"Then I'll do it myself! You'll find yourself on report for this, Eggerton!"

Another cheer now as puffs of smoke appeared beneath the helicopter. Two missiles streaked across the sky. The first skidded across a car park, crashed through a low wall, and obliterated a tea shoppe. The second ran true and plunged through the roof of the newly completed building.

Andrew banked steeply to avoid the explosion. "Tally-ho!" he cried. Eggerton slapped him hard. "Where am I?" The Prince blinked twice and looked around. "What happened?"

"Had another one of your spells, sir." Eggerton had regained the controls.

"Oh God," said Andrew. "What did I do this time?"

The jewelled amulet, it was said, had been presented to Queen Victoria by the Maharaja of Jodhpur as a token of his servitude. Later it was passed on by succession to Edward VII and then to George V. Edward VIII had attempted to slip it as a gift to that Simpson woman, but had been thwarted at the last moment by Queen Mary. She had entrusted it for safe keeping to the Queen, who, in turn, had bestowed it upon Diana on her wedding day. And so, when Prince William smashed it with a hammer, there was a considerable fuss.

The future monarch's howls summoned Charles who ran in from the garden. Diana was on all fours gingerly approaching the raging prince who was now swinging wildly in the direction of a Silesian vase thought to date from about 1740.

"Don't just stand there, Charles!" Diana hissed. "Do something!"

"There's a good boy, Wills. Give Mummy the hammer." Charles sensed it was no use.

The vase did not so much break as disintegrate into a fine powder. Wills dropped the hammer and fled.

"Dammit!" said Diana, "Where's Nanny Barnes when I need her?"

"You fired her," replied Charles. "You've fired everyone!"

"The child is perfectly hideous," said Diana. "A little beast!"

"And you want a third one?" Charles saw that his remark had hit home.

For just a moment Diana sagged in defeat. Then Charles saw her stiffen. "That look" came into her eyes.

"All right," she said. "Tell your precious mama she's won. We'll go to stupid old Canada!"

General Eric von Kleist of the West German Army watched with surprise and then considerable alarm as the British Chieftain tank thundered towards him. The elderly soldier was nearing the end of a brilliant military career. In 1940 his XIX Panzer Korps had slashed its way through France. Later he'd distinguished himself with the Hermann Goering division in Italy. Even a stint on the Eastern Front had left him unscathed. Post-war years found him attached to NATO headquarters in Brussels. It was by mere chance that he was now standing on the firing range at this precise spot.

"A little slower, Your Royal Highness!" Sarah could see the soldier beside her gesturing but she couldn't make out his words over the roar of the tank's engine. Besides, it was all she could do to peer through the periscope and grip the wheel with both hands. *My God! What's that? Some silly man is standing in the way.* Sarah searched in vain for the horn.

General von Kleist had sometimes imagined he would die this way — crushed beneath British armour, ground into the soil of the Fatherland. But not recently.

The tank passed over the general, continued on for a hundred yards or so, then turned. The engine coughed once and died. There was a moment's silence. Then the hatch clanged open and a kerchiefed head emerged from the turret. Sarah looked around. "Awfully sorry," she said.

It was thought fortunate by those present that not two hours later the princess received an urgent summons to London.

Rupert Mollusk watched idly as the ice in his whiskey and soda tinkled ever so slightly. It was only to be expected, he reasoned, seeing the drink was balanced on a plastic tray four miles above the North Atlantic. The Concorde would be landing in less than an hour and there was much to do. Mollusk frowned as he reviewed the events of the past few days. It had indeed been foolish to entrust those photos to the mail. They were the key to reversing the fortunes of his flagging flagship publication, *The London Sunday Muckraker*. Now they were in the hands of God knew who. It didn't bear thinking about. Never mind. If you want something done right in this world you must do it yourself. His hand caressed the maroon leather binder. Photographic evidence of randy royals in mid-romp was a publishing coup without doubt. And so it was that Rupert Mollusk was flying to London. With the originals.

At the far end of the social scale and many miles below, the Scugwells were enduring a patch of bad luck. It had been going on for nearly ten years. The combination of Mr. Scugwell's chronic unemployment and his wife's uncanny aptitude for producing yet more Scugwells had caused their already dim prospects to gutter out completely. On this particular morning they were discussing their reduced circumstances with unusual candour.

"Wha'cha mean you're knocked up?" sputtered Mr. Scugwell. "I told you we couldn't afford to have no more flamin' kids, you fat cow!"

"We could if you'd find some work, you lazy sod!" replied Mrs. Scugwell, demonstrating the strength of her opinion with a blow that knocked Mr. Scugwell into the telly.

"Right," said her husband, picking himself up and grabbing a fireplace poker, "so that's how you want to play it then." He bore down upon his wife with a terrible fury.

There was a genteel rap on the door. The Scugwells did not appear to hear it. The door opened.

"Hello," said Charles, "mind if we come in?"

For some time Charles had been obsessed by the plight of Britain's inner cities. It had begun with his first blurred glimpses of drab rows of flats from fast-moving motorcades and had resulted in this — surprise investigatory visits to the homes of the poor. He really did try to keep them simple. Just Charles, the driver, of course, three television people, what seemed to be about six reporters, one or two members of the local council, and a spy sent by Margaret Thatcher.

"Hope we're not interrupting anything," said Charles, extending his hand.

"We ain't done nothin'," said Mr. Scugwell.

Charles glanced about the room. "No," he said, "I can certainly see that. I wonder, my good fellow, would you either strike your wife with that poker or else lower it?"

Scugwell lowered it. Charles entered.

"Just popped by to see the wretched squalor you live in," Charles said. "Sort of a hobby of mine."

"You're ... you're him!" said Mrs. Scugwell, shrieking and pointing. She'd finally caught on.

"'Course it's him," said her husband. "He done the Threadbares up the street just last Thursday."

"Indeed I did," Charles replied. "Horrible place. Not a patch on yours, though."

"Not my fault," said Mr. Scugwell, "can't work. It's me vertebrates."

"I know what you mean," Charles commiserated. "Had the same thing myself. Polo accident. That how you got yours?"

"Want some tea?" Mrs. Scugwell interrupted.

"Jolly nice of you," Charles effused. "Yes, I believe there's nineteen of us."

While Mrs. Scugwell busied herself at the hotplate, Charles observed with interest as Mr. Scugwell pointed to the yellow sludge that dripped from the pipes. He tried his hand at backing up the water closet and dutifully peered down the hole where the rat came in.

When at last the visit was over, Mr. Scugwell, who had been building up his nerve, blurted out, "How 'bout givin' us a fiver, then?"

Charles pretended to search his pockets. "Sorry," he said, "actually I don't generally carry, uh, fivers. But thanks awfully for letting us drop by."

"Tea's ready," said Mrs. Scugwell.

"Goodbye," said Charles, heading for the door.

O f course I'm delighted," said the Queen and truly she was. She always enjoyed a triumph. "But do you really feel you're up to going to Canada so soon after ... losing the baby?"

"You needn't fuss," said Diana. "I was simply mistaken."

"Indeed you were," said the Queen.

Charles set to work to lighten the mood. "Well, actually it might be fun, going to Calgary and all. What is this Yahoo Days, Mama? Some sort of cowboy-and-Indian thing?"

The Queen examined the invitation. It was in the shape of a ten-gallon hat. "Well," she said, "it doesn't much sound like a festival of the arts."

"So it is just Calgary then?" Charles asked cautiously.

"Well, you know the Canadians," said the Queen, "they like to get their money's worth. There was mention of a stop in Ottawa and somewhere else... New Brunswick, I believe."

"Oh no! I won't do it! I can't do it! Oh, I feel faint!" Diana had much more to say but she was drowned out by an ear-piercing "thunk", "thunk", "thunk" that filled the room, rattling the windows and threatening the china.

"Oh, I am angry," said the Queen. "I've told Andrew repeatedly not to land his Sea King on The Mall."

"Hello, you lot!" Andrew bounded into the room displaying that infectious charm that everyone found so irritating. "Hello, Mama. Hello, Diana. Hear you've got a bun in the oven, what?"

"Don't be silly, Andrew," said the Queen. "Diana's not pregnant."

"But, Mama, I thought that's why you called me home. Thought we were going to celebrate."

"No," said the Queen. "You're hardly here to celebrate. I think it might be best if we wait for ... ah, here she is now."

"Hello, everyone!" It was Sarah, still in her battle fatigues. "Diana, I just heard. I'm so glad for you!" Diana turned to avoid the embrace.

"Diana's not pregnant, Sarah."

"But I thought..."

"Never mind," said the Queen. "I've called you home on an entirely different matter. Your father will speak to you, Andrew. I'll talk to Sarah. Ah, Philip. Andrew and Sarah are here."

"Hello, Papa." Andrew turned his charm on his father who had just entered the room.

"Hello, my boy. Hello, Diana. How's our little number three coming along then?"

"Diana's not pregnant, Philip," the Queen explained patiently.

"Not pregnant? What do you mean, not pregnant?"

Diana thought she would explode. She did.

"No, I am not pregnant. If you want babies have your own damn babies!" — this remark she hurled accusingly at Andrew and Sarah — "Yes, I am going to Canada. Dreary though it is, it's bound to be more congenial than this place."

"I think," said the Queen, "it might be best if we all have tea." And they did just that.

Rupert Mollusk looked through the bullet-proof glass of the *Muckraker* boardroom window. Beyond the triple strands of electrified barbed wire, past the minefield, stood the gun tower. *Comforting*, he thought. From where he stood he could just make out the tiny knot of union protesters near the front gate.

He was not pleased. He turned to confront the dozen faces lining the long table.

"Gentlemen," he said, "I am not pleased. As you know it has always been the policy of the *Muckraker* to seek out the truth, to hunt down the facts of any story and present them in an intelligent manner. And failing that, to make something up. But, gentlemen, judging by your most recent efforts this policy is simply not being followed." He leafed through a large folder. "'Queen Mum Off To Scotland.' Yes, very exciting, that. 'Liz Laid Low By Virus.' Yes, had to go and lie down when I read that one. No gentlemen, I am not pleased." Mollusk allowed a dramatic few seconds to pass. "Gentlemen," he said, and now he leaned forward, hands flat on the table, "I am here to take over. I personally will show you how a proper newspaper is run and I will do it beginning with these!"

Mollusk watched with satisfaction as the photos had their desired effect.

These were the moments that Margaret Thatcher cherished. To immerse oneself in a simple domestic chore, ah, this was bliss indeed. When the phone rang she was installing a laser surveillance system in the front hall.

"It's the Queen," said Dennis, covering the mouthpiece. His hands were still wet from the washing up.

"Tell her I'm out," said Margaret. She was busy studying the manual. It was in German.

"She's very insistent. Says it's urgent."

"Oh poop." Margaret knew when she was licked. She took the receiver.

"Your Majesty, I trust you are enjoying the unseasonably warm temperatures we've been experiencing?"

The Queen's tone was unmistakable.

"When I want a weather report, Prime Minister, I'll ring a meteorologist. In the meantime, it would seem a well-known publisher has every intention of running certain photographs in his so-called newspaper."

"Ah yes, the *Muckraker.*" Margaret was playing for time.

"Ah," said the Queen. "So you know all about the *Muckraker* then."

"Only by reputation, Your Majesty. We don't subscribe. I mean, Dennis sometimes picks it up, although I've asked him not to..."

"And what do you know of its publisher, one Rupert Mollusk?"

"I don't know him at all," Margaret replied, "although I've been an admirer of his union-bashing activities for years."

"Prime Minister" — the Queen was growing tired of the niceties — "what do you intend to do about this mess?"

"Do?" asked the Prime Minister. "Why nothing. Unfortunately my hands are tied. It is the policy of my government never to interfere with the free press."

"Oh?" asked the Queen. "And when did that start?"

"Yes," the Prime Minister continued, ignoring the question, "current policies dictate that I may only inform you of the situation."

"The pleasure, Prime Minister, is entirely yours. So, you intend to do nothing?"

The Prime Minister sought to bring a nuance of regret to her reply.

"Unfortunately, although I find the situation appalling, I shall only be following it with keen interest. Your Majesty? Hello?" *How very odd*, thought Margaret Thatcher, *we've been disconnected.*

W ell now, Andrew my boy, how are you getting on?" Philip always enjoyed these chats with this son. There was something refreshingly straightforward about Andrew. No artificial sophistication, no complex emotions, no visible sign of intelligence. "Still happy with naval life?"

"Oh yes, Papa. All the other lads think I'm a topper!"

"Yes," said Philip, "I remember my days at sea. Lots of fun. I recall one time we were in Alexandria. Belly dancer there, a real smasher. Well, one thing led to another..."

For a blissful minute Philip retreated to a mirage of towering minarets, heat, and sultry flesh. *What was that girl's name? Started with a "J." Jasmine? Jezebel? Joan?*

"Yes, Papa?"

Philip was jolted back to the present.

"... never mind. But that's what I wanted to talk to you about."

"Belly dancers?"

"Well, in a way. Your mother asked me to talk to you about...ahem, your sex life."

"Don't be silly, Papa." Andrew snorted. "You told me all

about that years ago. How the man gets on top, how the woman lies there and..."

"Yes, yes, my boy" — Philip was growing impatient — "I know that. What I'm trying to say is that I'm aware that you've had your, well, adventures in the past. I mean Koo Stark and the others. But now that you're a married man I only hope you're all through with that...well, that sex business. I mean, you are, aren't you?"

"Oh yes, Papa. I don't need sex anymore. I've got Sarah."

"If that's the case," said Philip, "how do you explain these?" Philip laid out the photos on the table one by one. Andrew studied them with interest.

"Well?" said Philip.

"Oh dear," said Andrew, "the camera wasn't kind to Edward."

B ut don't you see, my dear? Andrew is right. It *is* Edward."

Philip had burst in on the Queen who was lecturing Sarah. Now Philip was shoving the photos under her nose.

"Yes, Mama, I'm sure it's Edward." Andrew had followed Philip into the room. "Those watery eyes, that pouty mouth."

The Queen examined the photos again, this time with a magnifying glass. "Well," she said, "I just naturally assumed it was you, Andrew, but yes, you might be right. I do believe it is your brother."

"I must say I'm rather pleased." Philip was beaming. "Didn't think the boy had it in him. Damn fine show."

"Don't be tiresome, Philip," said the Queen. "Andrew or Edward or whoever it is, the *Muckraker* still intends to publish these photos. That is unless..."

"Unless what, Mama?" Andrew's curiosity was aroused.

"Nothing to concern you, dear." The fewer who knew what the Queen was about to do, the better.

"All the same, I'm very pleased." Philip was at it again. "Must congratulate the boy, give him a Duke of Edinburgh Achievement Award, something like that."

But the Queen was no longer listening. She had an idea.

Rupert Mollusk was sure he'd thought of everything. The massive advertising campaign was well under-way. He'd personally supervised the layout of the photo spread. He'd even written the copy himself, under a pseudonym of course.

Now, as he settled down to a well-deserved brandy, Mollusk knew that within hours his *London Sunday Muckraker* would once again be a journalistic force to be reckoned with.

There was just one thing he'd not anticipated. The heavy, cream-coloured bond envelope containing a letter summoning him to an immediate audience with the Queen had arrived before he could take his first sip.

Charles knew the gentle tap upon his study door could only be Jessop. Dear Jessop, faithful Jessop. For more than twenty years he had served as Charles's secretary and friend. The man did not walk so much as glide and right now he was skimming across the room with a pile of books for Charles.

"Excuse me, Master Charles," he said, "I've managed to secure that reference material you requested for your speech to the Canadian parliament."

"Wonderful, Jessop." Charles scanned the spines. Omar

Kyam; *UFOs: The Real Story*; *Out on a Limb*, by Shirley MacLaine…yes they all seemed to be there. "Thank you, Jessop," said Charles. "Whatever would I do without you?"

"I'm afraid you're about to find out, sir."

At first Jessop's words didn't register but then Charles stopped writing and looked up.

"Find out? Whatever do you mean, Jessop?"

"I've been let go, sir."

"Let go? Don't be ridiculous! You've been with me, what? Twenty years?"

"Twenty-five, sir." Jessop bristled at the thought of someone lopping five years off his tenure.

"Exactly," said Charles. "So what's all this nonsense then?"

"'She' let me go, sir."

"Diana? But why?"

"I called Wills a little shit, sir."

"But he is a little shit."

"And," said Jessop, "I struck him."

Charles sprang to his feet. "Struck him? My son? Jolly good! You don't know how I've longed to do that! What was it like?"

Jessop allowed himself the briefest hint of a smile. "Very satisfying, sir."

"Well," said Charles, "We simply can't have this. I'll talk to Diana, straighten out this whole mess."

"If you don't mind, sir, I think it better if we leave things the way they are. Life hasn't been the same since 'she' came."

"No, it hasn't," Charles agreed. Charles and Jessop shared a silent, misty moment. "But, Jessop, what will you do? How will you manage?"

"Oh, don't worry about me, sir." Jessop's tone was reassuring. "I have every reason to believe I shall have a handsome private income of my own in the very near future."

Have some more mutton. Let's get some flesh on those bones."

Diana looked with horror at the slithery piece of meat that Philip was thrusting in her direction.

"No, thank you," she said.

"Give it to me, Papa." It was Andrew. "Look, Diana hasn't even touched her first piece yet."

"There he goes, the Duke of Pork," said Sarah. She too was ready for more.

"Diana's off meat again, Papa," said Charles.

"Well, I'm not," said Sarah. "Give it to me."

"Off meat?" said Philip. "You're turning into one of these bloody aner, uh, anor…uh…"

"The word is 'anorexic' and I'm not," said Diana. "I'm just fabulously thin." The table exploded in laughter. "Well, if you're all going to behave like a lot of common boors," Diana snapped, "then I'd just as soon go home. Charles?"

The Queen's voice cut through the bedlam. "Diana is quite right. If this continues I shall leave as well." Silence.

This dinner had been the Queen's idea; a last chance to fill her reluctant voyagers with good food and sound advice. They'd had the first; it was time for the second.

"I sometimes think," the Queen said, "of this family as riding a great long bicycle, all of us pedalling madly away." The Queen was using her "this will interest you greatly" voice.

"A bicycle, Mama?" asked Charles.

"Yes, one of those long jobs with all the seats," said Andrew helpfully.

"Yes, Andrew," the Queen said patiently. "That's exactly what I mean. Everyone has to work jolly hard to keep it going. Now, from time to time someone climbs aboard who doesn't want to pedal. That person becomes a dead weight."

"She means you, tubby!" Sarah shot a pellet of bread at her husband's head.

"I'm not tubby," said Andrew. "I'm just fabulously fat."

More laughter.

The Queen "ahemed."

Silence again.

Now the Queen fixed her gaze on Diana.

"Then, of course, there are some people who want to take their bit of bicycle and ride away in a different direction altogether. Well, I simply cannot allow that to happen. And do you know why?"

"Why, Mama?" asked Charles.

"Because," said the Queen, "it's my bicycle."

"But, Mama," Andrew chimed, "where is this bicycle? I've never seen it."

"Shut up, you idiot!"

"What a twit!"

"Mama's making an analogy!"

Philip rapped on his plate with a spoon. "I'd like to propose a toast."

Glasses were hastily filled and raised.

"Now with you two going off to Canada tomorrow and all, I'd just like to say, wherever you may wander, wherever you may roam, if you screw things up, don't bother coming home."

"Philip!" said the Queen.

"It's all right," said Charles. "Papa's only joking."

"I'm not," muttered Philip.

"We won't screw up," said Charles. "And anyway, the Canadians aren't so bad."

"Bloody awful people," said Philip.

"At least they're not Americans."

"Ghastly bunch," said Philip.

"Or Australians." At this a chorus of howls went up.

"Oooh, Australians!"

"God save us!"

"Absolutely horrid!"

"Yes," said the Queen. "I admit the Australians are an acquired taste, but it's the Canadians that concern us now.

I've made some last-minute notes. Diana, are you listening?"

The Queen put on her glasses and read from a small notebook. "They still have the same Prime Minister, of course. Only the usual courtesies for him, I think. He'll not be around much longer. You'll find the country in its usual state: poverty in the east, anger in the west…that sort of thing. You're bound to receive some bizarre gifts. This time I won't have them left behind in hotel rooms. Bring them home. We'll sort them out here. Wear any and all garments they ask you to put on…no matter how peculiar, and above all, keep smiling." The Queen managed one of her own and then added limply, "Have fun."

There was but one drawback to the handsome rooms Jessop had taken two days before in Richmond Hill. It was that sometimes one could hear the distant roar of the jets lifting off from nearby Heathrow. It is just possible that Jessop, too, endured the dull, thundering lift off of the Canadian Forces 707 as it climbed with its royal cargo en route to Ottawa. But if he did hear, Jessop surely took no notice for he was staring, awed, at the blank piece of paper he'd just rolled into his newly purchased typewriter.

He took a hesitant peck, then another. Soon his typing gained speed and confidence.

"She-Bitch of the Windsors." Yes, that was good. "The Memoirs of a Loyal Royal Servant." There. The hard part, beginning, was done. He hadn't been sure he could do it. But, he could indeed.

"I will never forget my first glimpse of the woman who would one day be known as Diana, Princess of Wales…"

By now the subject of his literary endeavours was over Land's End.

Princess Margaret Rose stared long and hard at the old woman confronting her. What could she say to comfort that sallow face, those heavy-lidded eyes, the pinched mouth? And the hair. The once lustrous chestnut mane now a matted tangle of greying straw. She forced herself to turn away from the mirror, a gift of the Miami Chamber of Commerce. There was but one thing to do.

She eased herself into the steaming bath water. It would be easier this way. She'd wait until she was truly relaxed and then…*Now where is that package of razor blades?* Decisions come easy when one's alternatives are reduced to a single option. She guessed she'd always known that this was the only way. And now she was doing it, with slow, deliberate strokes. Princess Margaret Rose was shaving her head.

If there was a constant in the Queen's life then it was Susan. Friend, confidante, loving companion; she'd even accompanied the Queen on her honeymoon so many years before. But now the Queen was concerned. Susan was slowing down. She'd lost a good part of her sight and had turned somewhat arthritic. Susan was a corgi. She was forty-two.

Lately Susan had taken to sleeping in peculiar places. She'd lurch about a room for a time and then collapse with a contented wheeze. None of this, of course, was known to Rupert Mollusk. Had it been, his left foot might never have come into sharp contact with the sleeping corgi as he crossed the room to meet the Queen. He might never have been catapulted forward, suspended for a brief moment in space, and then deposited face down at her majesty's feet.

"I'm so dreadfully sorry. I don't know what to say." The Queen was doing her best to comfort the whimpering corgi she cradled in her arms. Mollusk struggled to his knees.

"Your Majesty, allow me to say what a great pleasure it is

for me to meet with you in the flesh," said the publisher, profferring his hand. It was ignored.

"Yes, it must be very exciting for you," said the Queen. "Sit down, Mr. Mollusk." Mollusk had prepared his opening remarks and was determined to continue.

"And if I may," he said, "let me tell you of the great respect I have, not only for yourself…"

"Yes, Mr. Mollusk," said the Queen. "I'm quite aware of the respect you show towards my family and myself. I have a few examples of that respect here." The Queen reached for a file folder. She removed several clippings and began to read aloud. "'Fat Fergie Fasting', 'Andy's Spanking Good Time'…"

"Uh, yes," replied Mollusk. "Most regrettable. The work of overly zealous reporters. I need not tell Your Majesty how they can be."

"Indeed, you need not," said the Queen, "nor overly zealous photographers."

Mollusk knew what was coming. He girded his loins.

"Your Majesty?"

"The pictures of my son Edward. Do you intend to publish them, Mr. Mollusk?"

Mollusk had been preparing himself for this moment. He knew the future freedom of the British press rested on his answer. He knew he must be decisive, firm.

"Yes, Your Majesty," he said, "I do." His eyes met the level gaze of the Queen. "I mean, I'm not sure."

"Publish them," said the Queen. Mollusk was suitably disarmed.

"Publish them, Your Majesty? But I thought…"

"You thought correctly, Mr. Mollusk. I had intended to forbid you to publish those pictures but I've had a change of mind."

"I don't understand."

"Mr. Mollusk. Thanks to publications such as your *Muckraker* Edward has unfortunately been branded a wimp. It is time that image was corrected. Those photographs are just the ticket."

"Let me get this straight, Your Majesty," said Mollusk struggling to understand. "You want me to publish the pictures with your endorsement?"

"Certainly not," said the Queen. "We shall protest most vigorously."

"Yet I am to publish the pictures anyway?"

The Queen nodded. "I think you're finally beginning to get our meaning," she said.

"I see. Yes. I see."

"But, Mr. Mollusk, be warned" — the Queen rose. Mollusk shot to his feet — "if even a single word of our little meeting should appear in your publication..."

"Believe me, Your Majesty, when I say..."

"...even a single word, Mr. Mollusk..."

"Yes?"

"...then the *Muckraker* shall have for its publisher, a gelding."

A moment passed and then Mollusk laughed, heartily and with relief. So it was true what they said. The Queen really did have a marvellous sense of humour. Bubbly yet biting and so unexpected.

It was some time before he realized that the Queen was not laughing with or at him.

For heaven's sake, Diana, at least try to smile. Please, darling." Charles always likened these moments to performing on stage. Those final few seconds of waiting in the wings as the plane sat on the tarmac, audience expectation building, the door thrown open, show time. Inevitably Diana was irritable.

"I don't see why I should smile. That dreadful Mulroney

man's out there with his perky little wife, Mylar."

"It's Mila, darling, 'Meeeela.' Try to remember." And now the door was open. Sunlight streamed into the aircraft along with the thin cheers of school children conscripted for the occasion.

"Here we go," said Charles. "Smile."

And smile Diana did. Beautifully. Charles watched with pride as Diana descended the stairs with elegance and grace, smiling and waving. By God she could turn it on when she wanted to. And now they'd reached the red carpet. Diana was extending her hand to the lady in the flowery hat and billowing skirt.

"How wonderful to see you again, Mila."

Governor General Madame Sauvé was somewhat taken aback at being addressed in this manner but she managed her curtsey all the same.

And so, the elected members of this great House…" Charles had been pleased with his speech thus far. The Canadian parliamentarians had given him sustained applause for his call for more funding into psychic research, had listened with interest as he described the reasons why George III was not mad, and had even favoured him with a standing ovation on his call for a Canadian Professional Polo League. "I would urge you to contemplate together the peace and harmony of the universe. I thank you."

Charles had every reason to confidently expect prolonged applause. It came then as some surprise when the man in

the front row, in the tight-fitting suit, rose to his feet.

"Mr. Speaker," he said, "Would it not be better to contemplate the 9.4 per cent unemployed in this country who are unable to…"

Boos and catcalls rained through the chamber.

"Mr. Turner!" the Speaker's voice cut through. "This is not question period. Kindly sit down!"

Somewhere between the broiled sea bass Baie-Comeau and the meringue things with the fruit glopped on top, Diana started to get those old Expo feelings again. The Prime Minister had been droning into her left ear all night. Something about trading things to the United States for free.

"… an open and equitable understanding between two great democracies," he was saying, "the single longest undefended…"

Diana was reminded of a man who had once tried to sell her a pair of sensible shoes. She looked about. Charles was in an animated discussion with Mila. Good. It was her turn to put up with his prattle about hydroponic farming and astral soul travel or what have you. But what to do about the woman's dreary husband.

Diana's eyes rolled ceiling-ward. She sighed loudly. Her head lolled forward. She made a point of collapsing to her left. Conversation ceased. There were a few gasps, calls for assistance.

Just as she closed her eyes Diana noted with satisfaction that the Prime Minister had stopped talking.

Philip had always craved companionship of this sort. Someone well able to toss back the claret, who didn't blanch at his colourful stories and knew how to appreciate a fine cigar. And in his daughter, Anne, he'd found such a person. Philip had motored down to Gatcombe Park that afternoon, one of his surprise flying visits, and had discovered, to his delight, that she was "Fog"-less. Mark was away somewhere autographing porcelain horses. It was something he was especially good at. An icy rain had been falling for some hours, whipped up by a steady wind. They'd decided to go walking.

"You've too much on your plate these days," said Philip, struggling with his Hunter boots in the muck.

"Nonsense," said Anne, setting a brisk pace, "it's not so much. There's the Save the Badger Fund of course and I have the Druids on Tuesday nights. There's the Daughters of The S.A.S., the Tea Cozy Preservation Foundation, the Guild Of Alchemists, the David Lean Trust...that's about it."

"And don't forget the Lonely Seaman's Society," Philip reminded her. "No, it's too much, Anne. I insist you give one of them up."

"Give one of them up?" Anne stopped and turned. "To whom?"

"Well, to Sarah."

"What on earth for?" asked Anne.

"It's your mother's idea, really. Sarah's a good girl, but she's got a wild streak. Having something to do just might keep her in line. It wouldn't have to be anything big. Just something she couldn't possibly screw up."

Anne thought for a moment as the rain pounded into their faces with renewed vigour. "Well," she said at last, "I suppose I could give her one of my diseases."

"Splendid," said Philip. "I like the sound of that. By God, I wish the rest of them were more like you."

"I'm afraid there's only one of me," said Anne.

"You're right there," replied her father. "They broke the mould when they made you."

"Well, certainly around my chin they must have," said Anne ruefully, as they turned and headed back towards the house.

I t had been Cynthia's idea, really. Cynthia Robertson Marmalade. She and Florence Belmondo had been visiting Sarah in her rooms at the palace when Cynthia said, "I know! Let's disguise ourselves and walk about the city!"

"You're mad!" cried Florence, but Sarah said, "Yes, let's," and out came the heavy boots and old macintoshes. Hair was pinned under hats and off they went, slipping into the real world discreetly through a side door.

They headed down Buckingham Palace Road towards Victoria Station. Three bearded men, their high voices shrieking hysterically.

How exhilarating, thought Sarah, *to walk the streets, no one the wiser*. She found the danger delicious.

"Let's have a drink." Sarah pointed to a pub. By now she was feeling bold.

"Do you think we dare?" asked Florence, but Sarah was already leading the way.

Once inside Sarah shouldered her way to the front and, managing her gruffest voice said, "Three g and ts, my good fellow, and make it snappy."

"At once, Duchess," said the barman.

Several gins later and Sarah felt the fetters of palace life falling away. How frightfully coincidental then, that as they were leaving the pub, they should run across childhood chums Stinky Whitworth-Soames and Bunny Weller in Stinky's De Lorean. Within moments they were thundering towards Soho, Stinky hooting the horn as pedestrians dived for cover.

"Out of the way, you wankers!" Sarah shouted, her head protruding from the sun roof.

Stinky parked the De Lorean on the sidewalk outside Il Duce, the restaurant that Cynthia had suggested....

"A bottle of your finest Bordeaux for my three uncles," Bunny shouted to the maître d'. Bunny was considered something of a wit.

It was a superb meal marred only by the waiter's failure to appreciate Bunny's impeccable mimicry of him. But then the bun fight with a far table, instigated by Sarah, had not gone down well either.

Then it was off into the night, the De Lorean roaring and Bunny showering passers-by with champagne.

How wonderful, thought Sarah, *to be doing normal, down-to-earth things again.*

At Methadone, the new club on Sloane Street, the lights pulsed and the music pounded as Sarah danced with God knows who. Her disguise still seemed to be doing the job although by now the pins had come undone and her auburn tresses bounced on her shoulders.

"Ride the groove!" Sarah shouted to no one in particular.

Stinky had always been a little crazy, but this was truly insane. It was three in the morning and the De Lorean was circling Trafalgar Square at incredible speed. Music from the Alpine stereo system ricocheted off the walls of South Africa House and the National Gallery.

"Stop this car at once!" shouted Sarah, suddenly sober. "Stop this car!"

Stinky obeyed as the De Lorean's bonnet came into crunching contact with the base of Nelson's Column.

After the noise came the silence. Sarah was first aware of the hiss of escaping steam and then the rise and fall of approaching sirens. She looked around. The others had fled. *Oh no*, she thought, *what have I done?*

The remainder of the evening Sarah mercifully remembered hardly at all, although reports of a curious bearded man darting through Admiralty Arch and in and out among the trees along the Mall, reached the police too late for them to investigate.

"Thank you, God" said Sarah, as she slid into bed and watched the room go round and round.

A nd you weren't spotted?" asked the Queen.
"I'm certain we weren't," came the reply, "although three of my men were observing the subject at all times, ready to move in if required."

"Excellent," said the Queen, "you've done very well."

"Thank you, Your Majesty," said the detective. "Will you require me any longer?"

"I shouldn't think so," said the Queen. "I would think Sarah's had quite enough adventure for some time to come."

S carcely a single tourist approaching Buckingham Palace from the monument has taken note of the wing to one's right, facing north. Most concentrate their attention on the great iron gates, confident that some royal will appear at any instant. Lionel Stubbs knew better. He'd concentrated his attention on the north wing for some weeks. He knew that on the second floor was the Queen's bedroom. It was very important that the twenty-eight-year-old unemployed lorry driver meet with her majesty. He had something he wanted to show her.

Well, Philip, it's been a tiring day, think I'll turn in." The Queen stifled a yawn.

"Right, darling." Philip didn't look up. "Think I'll stay up and work a bit on this."

The Queen leaned over his shoulder.

"Yes, what is that you've been so busy at?"

"Speech for the Lord Mayor's banquet. Rather good if I say so myself."

"What is the subject?"

"I've called it 'Get Your Finger Out, or What's Wrong with the British Working Man.'"

"Oh dear," said the Queen. She went to bed.

It was an indulgence of the Queen's, during her summer stays at Sandringham, to be awakened each morning by a piper playing beneath her window. And for a few bleary moments that's where she believed she was at first. But then the Queen made out the shadows of her own palace bedroom. There was noise coming from the window all right — a series of horrid grunts followed by loud panting — suggestive of, but certainly not a piper.

"Go away, Philip," said the Queen. "I've had a hard day."

"Hey you, Queen, wake up!"

Evidently it was not Philip. A feeling of revulsion surged through the Queen's body, much like the time when Jimmy Carter had tried to kiss her. She sat up and flicked on the lamp. Yes, now she was able to make out the nasty little man crouching near the window.

"Who are you?" asked the Queen.

"Never you mind," he replied. "I've got somethin' to show you."

"Go away," said the Queen.

"It's somethin' you want, somethin' you need."

"How very tiresome," said the Queen. "All right, get on

with it. Show me what you will and then be off."

"How do you like this then?"

The Queen leaned forward for a better look.

"Yes, very nice. About average, I'd say. Now put on your trousers and get out, my man."

"Oh no. Not quite yet, Queen. Why don't you admit it? You want it, right?"

"Want? That?" asked the Queen. "Certainly not. It will be of much more use to you than it ever would be to me."

"Go on," said the little man, "You know what I mean. Take off your nightie, then, and put on your crown!"

"Ah," said the Queen. "Why didn't you say what you wanted in the first place? It would have saved us so much time."

"You mean you're...that is, willin'?"

"Well," said the Queen, "it's a most interesting proposition and one that should be discussed at leisure. What do you say to a cup of tea?" The Queen mustered a smile.

"Why, yes. I mean, if you're havin' one, yes."

"Excellent," she replied. "I wonder if you'd do me a great kindness and push that button just beside you."

Lionel looked about. He was eager to please.

"This one?"

The Queen nodded.

The screech of the klaxon horns was deafening.

A half a world away, Diana had been sleeping as well. From hasty consultations the previous evening it had appeared that Diana's swoon would be forgotten, that it would be best to carry through with a full day's activities. The next twenty-four hours had been a blur of shrieking children and popping flashbulbs, punctuated by an unpleasant encounter with a lewd pensioner.

Now at last she could sleep. Diana was dreaming, a

nightmare really. Millions and millions of Canadians, all dressed in ski jackets, stretching over a rocky, pine-dotted horizon. They wanted Diana, wanted to tear away a part of her, a little piece for each of them. Now they were touching her with their damp matted mittens. Diana flailed about, fighting them off.

"Diana, for God's sake wake up!" It was Charles. And there were other faces as well; the Governor General, her equerry, the ubiquitous Mulroneys. The remaining twenty-five hundred faces Diana didn't recognize, but they were staring all the same. Only the Royal Winnipeg Ballet, oblivious of the commotion, continued to clump around the Arts Centre stage, meticulously recreating a folk dance unknown to pioneers.

"It's all right, she didn't faint," Charles assured the others.

"Just sort of nodded off. Rather warm in here, what?" A moment later, smiling and nodding completed, he whispered, "Diana, how could you! In front of all these people!"

"For heaven's sake, Charles," Diana shot back, "you're the one who ought to wake up. When will you realize this whole thing's just a ruddy great bore?"

The early-morning summons to the palace had set the Prime Minister's mind racing. What matter of urgency could demand an audience so early in the day? Did storm clouds once again loom over Port Stanley? Did Muammar al-Qaddafi require a second rap on the knuckles? Had the IRA engaged in more beastliness? Margaret Thatcher could only dream and hope.

"Your Majesty, may I say how wonderfully well you look this morning?"

"You may not," said the Queen. "I couldn't possibly look well. I didn't sleep a wink all night."

"Oh," said the Prime Minister. "May I ask why?"

"Last night," said the Queen, "there was a man in my room."

"Congratulations, Your Majesty."

"He was not," said the Queen, "a man of my own choosing."

"Oh," said Margaret Thatcher. She had no idea where this was leading.

"Fortunately," the Queen continued, "he turned out to be a harmless lunatic, but he might have been a terrorist."

Terrorism. Ah. Now the Prime Minister felt she was back on firmer ground.

"Well, as you know, Your Majesty, I have strong views on the subject of terrorism."

"For or against?" asked the Queen.

The Prime Minister pushed on. "I have left definite instructions that should I be kidnapped there must be no negotiations or payment of ransom."

"Don't worry, Prime Minister. I shall see to it that not a penny is spent on your behalf."

Margaret Thatcher thought she detected just a hint of a Queenly smirk. She bowed ever so slightly.

"I am deeply grateful, Your Majesty."

The Queen was now offering more than a hint of scowl.

"The point of the matter is, Prime Minister, what are you doing about my family's security?"

The Prime Minister mulled the question over. "Well," she said, "let me see. There are, of course, our submarines armed with Polaris missiles, ever vigilant —"

"I was thinking of something a little closer to home," the Queen interrupted "What I want is a complete review of the palace security system. I want appropriate measures taken, a full report, and I want it now."

The Prime Minister found herself bowing a second time. "Yes, Your Majesty. At once."

And now the Queen's face softened. "I think," she said, "as it's rather early a little breakfast might be in order."

"Oh yes," said the Prime Minister. "How very thoughtful."

The Queen tinkled a tiny bell. The door opened.

"Breakfast please, Jackson," said the Queen. "Eggs, toast, bacon and coffee…for one."

R upert Mollusk had left strict instructions that he was not to be disturbed. The quivering little man in the chair opposite him would require his undivided attention.

"Now see here, Jessop," he was saying, "I gave you an advance of twenty thousand pounds for your memoirs. I suggest you get cracking on them."

In truth Mollusk had scarcely recognized Jessop when he came in. The man seemed utterly broken, a caricature of his former self. He wasn't sure where Jessop had been keeping himself, but it certainly wasn't at a luxury spa.

"Please, Mr. Mollusk," — Jessop seemed close to tears — "I've had second thoughts. You don't realize the great risk I'm taking in even writing them. Let me return the money."

"Money I can get anywhere," said the publisher. "It's your memoirs I want."

"But sir, I'm breaking my sacred word!"

"Mr. Jessop," said Mollusk, "I do that three times a day."

The intercom buzzed annoyingly. "Thelma," said Mollusk, "I told you I was not to be disturbed."

"But sir," the unseen Thelma squawked back, "it's our man in Canada. He says he's on to something."

Ah! It must be Geoffrey.

Sending a reporter on the royal tour was one thing. Sending a lip reader was vintage Mollusk. It was about to pay off.

"Yes Geoffrey, what have you got?" Mollusk shouted into the receiver. "She said what? Let me take that down. Canada…a ruddy…great…bore. You're sure those were her exact words? Well, it hardly matters, does it? Good work, Geoffrey. Well done." He slammed down the receiver. He clapped his hands. "Oh my," he said, "I can't believe my good fortune. Oh my. Yes, I must have done something good sometime to someone to deserve this," and then added a moment later, "though for the life of me I can't think what, when, or to whom."

Alone, ignored, at the far end of the room, Jessop sobbed uncontrollably.

Thus far the Queen was not pleased. Her tour of the new palace security measures with a certain Inspector Hargraves was not going well. The Queen suspected the Prime Minister hadn't exactly broken the bank on this one.

"And what is this man doing?" the Queen asked. She'd caught sight of a man staring at a television.

"Ah," said Hargraves, "now he is a part of our new video security unit. He will observe that television monitor twenty-four hours a day."

"What is he observing at present?" asked the Queen. The Inspector moved closer for a better look.

"Snooker, Your Majesty."

Finally they'd arrived at the Queen's bedroom. Hargraves was ill at ease. "I believe this is the window through which the intruder entered?" he asked, knowing full well it was.

"It is," said the Queen. "What have you done to secure it?" The Inspector lifted the window.

"If Your Majesty will look down there…" The Queen stuck her head out.

"What is that supposed to be?" she asked.

"Camel bells, Your Majesty, strung along a length of wire. No one can enter the window without setting them off."

"And when I hear this tell-tale tinkling, Inspector, what am I then to do?"

"Ah yes, well," the Inspector moved to the bed. "Then you'd just reach beneath your bed like so" — he fumbled about on the floor a moment — "and you would produce this."

"What in God's name is that?" asked the Queen.

"An Uzi submachine gun, Your Majesty." The Queen had had enough.

"Inspector, do you mean to tell me that this is the full extent of the Prime Minister's security precautions?"

"There is one other measure we have taken, Your Majesty," said Hargraves, "and though it's never been done before we do feel that it is prudent."

"And what is that?" asked the Queen.

"We've decided to lock the front door."

Princess Margaret Rose was coming out of the closet. It took courage, but she'd decided it was time. After all, one couldn't stand around looking at one's old clothes forever. The crepe Chanel, for instance. She'd once thought Diana might like it. How could she have been so stupid? Oh, certainly Diana would have been gracious enough about receiving it: "Oh thank you, Margaret. How perfectly wonderful. Look at the marvellous work here." But what fun she'd have had later with Sarah. "Can you believe the silly old cow actually thinking for one minute that I would want her smelly old things?"

The gowns that had once knocked Mayfair on its ear were now hanging in lonely splendour in a cedar-lined closet.

How like myself, thought Margaret Rose.

She moved to the writing table. The setting sun cut through the leaded glass, filling the room with golden melancholy. Margaret picked up the fountain pen, a gift of the mayor of Canberra. It would be some time before she

set it to paper. She'd always found it difficult to say
goodbye.

Eight months before the Queen had paid a state visit
to the sheikdom of Dubai and for a dreamy moment
that's where she believed she was.

The endless sands, the searing heat, the gentle lilt of
camel bells. But then the Queen made out the shadows of
her own palace bedroom. She'd been right about the camel
bells, but these were the ones just outside her window.

"Who's there?" she asked. There was no answer. Someone
was scaling the wall. The Queen reached for the Uzi.
"Who's there?" she demanded a second and final time.

Her answer came as a great smashing of glass, an
enormous crash and a loud "bloody hell" as a body
tumbled into the room. The Queen fired. The recoil from
the Uzi threw her back across the bed. A spray of bullets
smashed up the wall and into the ceiling.

"Don't shoot! Don't shoot!"

The Queen dropped the gun and flicked on the light.
"Philip!" she said. "What on earth are you doing?"

"Trying to get into my own damn home! Some idiot's
locked the front door!"

Honestly, Diana, I couldn't believe it when they told
me! 'Canada A Ruddy Great Bore, Says Di,' right
across the front page of the *Muckraker*."

Charles had been going on about it all morning and
Diana was no longer interested. Besides, it was almost
impossible to maintain a conversation while waving out
opposite windows of the car.

"Do stop going on about it, Charles." Diana smiled

fetchingly. "Canada *is* a ruddy great bore."

"But, darling," Charles was almost pleading, "if word of what you said gets out here there'll be hell to pay."

"Don't be stupid, Charles. The Canadians have no idea what goes on in the English press. By the way, what have we got on next?"

Charles consulted a small notebook. "Let's see...three-minute stop, walkabout, two choirs, children and cripples."

"Piece of cake," said Diana.

Charles was first to take notice of the unusually large crowd as the car slowed to a stop. "Quite a turn-out," he remarked.

"Maybe now you'll stop your worrying," said Diana.

"How are you all then?" Charles gave the crowd a wave. "Hello."

The first tomato grazed Diana's ear. The second found its mark.

For Governor General Madame Sauvé it had been an exhausting year. A trip to mainland China had left her reeling. Her ongoing battles with that most presidential of prime ministers had sapped her strength. Spring had found her participating in the opening of parliament. This evening found her participating in the opening of a sofa bed.

"Pull harder from your end!" she demanded of her husband, but it was clear the poor man was already doing his best.

"Don't think we ought to force it," he said. "Better have another look at those instructions."

"Want me to have a go?" Charles had suddenly appeared in his pyjamas. He'd come downstairs for cocoa.

"No, no, quite all right, we'll manage," the Sauvés chorused, simultaneously but silently regretting their choices of night-time attire.

"Wants a good pull does it?" asked Charles, taking firm hold of the middle. "Now altogether on the count of three. One, two, three."

From somewhere inside the reluctant sofa there came a deep metallic "sproing." A sad little platform flopped forward, almost knocking them off their feet.

"There you go. Right as rain," said the Prince, pleased with his efforts.

"Yes, thank you," said the Governor General. She was eyeing the mattress, which now keeled alarmingly to one side.

"Awfully good of you, putting us up and all," Charles went on. "Hope we're not too much bother."

· "Not at all. No trouble whatsoever." The Governor General wished he would go away. "Please think of our home as your home."

"As a matter of fact it is," said Charles.

He was all set to explain the historical implications of his reply when he was interrupted by a concrete block that shattered the window above his head, slammed into the far wall, and clattered to a rest between the Sauvés. Charles knelt to examine it. A note had been taped to one side. It bore a simple message. "Send the bitch home."

"Awfully sorry," said Charles. "Believe this was meant for Diana. I'll just take it up to her then. Night all."

Diana's televised statement was unprecedented and, coming as it did in the middle of "The Young and the Restless," enjoyed a wide viewership. Made to seem frail behind the large desk selected for that purpose, she had chosen to wear a cobalt-blue Victor Edelstein original. She spoke slowly and precisely.

"In recent days, I have been quoted as saying that Canada is a ruddy great bore. I must tell you that this is categorically a misrepresentation. At no time did I say that Canada is a ruddy great bore. It was that dreadful show you forced me to sit through. That was the ruddy great bore. Thank you."

A brief smile and she was gone.

The sudden appearance of her mother had startled the Queen. The Queen Mother had spent the better part of the month laid low by a virus. Now, suddenly, here she was, a flushed and beaming pile of turquoise chiffon.

"Mummy, what on earth have you been up to? You're all wind-blown and the petals in your hat are askew."

"That lovely Elton John drove me over in his new motor car with the top down. Such fun! I haven't had such a good time since we buried the Simpson woman."

"Sit down, Mummy," said the Queen. "Have some tea."

"Nonsense. I'll have a gin and tonic." The Queen glanced at the clock.

"Do you think it wise to be drinking this early in the day?"

"Yes, dear," said the Queen Mother. "I'm quite sure it is."

"But, Mummy, you've been so ill."

The Queen Mother threw up her hands.

"I'm fit as a fiddle and ready to get back into harness. What have you got for me? I'm champing at the bit."

"Well," said the Queen, "I don't really know. There's the Gathering of the Clans in Aberdeen."

"Fiddle faddle," said the Queen Mother. "That's small potatoes. I've thought it over and I want to do a tour."

"A tour? But where?" asked the Queen.

"South Africa."

"South Africa?" The Queen swallowed hard. "But, Mummy, you can't go there!"

"And why not, I'd like to know?" The Queen Mother

sulked. "We always used to go there in the old days and had such a lovely time."

"But it's different now," said the Queen. "There's trouble."

"I know all about that," said the Queen Mother. "I've been watching it on the television. I've seen those poor people and their suffering and I want to help."

Now the Queen was touched.

"Mummy, that's so good of you. I feel the same as you, but there's little we can do. And you must remember, those poor people have fine leaders of their own, Bishop Tutu for instance."

The Queen Mother shuddered. "Oh, the dreadful man! Stirring up trouble, running amuck..."

"Mummy!" The Queen was shocked.

"The man's a Hottentot!" said the Queen Mother.

"If that's the way you feel then why do you want to go?" asked the Queen.

"Why to help those poor people of course."

"Which poor people?"

"Why, the white people, of course."

The Queen tinkled a tiny bell. The door opened.

"Gin and tonic," said the Queen, "for two."

L ord Louis Mountbatten of Burma had been dead for eight years, but was still hanging around. His continued spiritual existence had come as no surprise to him and it allowed him the advantage of maintaining contact with Charles. In times of great crises or when he was bored, Lord Louis would drop by dressed in the regalia of his colourful past. Tonight he'd arrived as the Viceroy of India. They were discussing Diana.

"You've got to put your foot down, let her know who's boss," said Lord Louis, "the way I did with my own Edwina back in 'forty-seven. I said to her, 'Edwina, you've got to stop having it off with that Nehru chap. We may be handing India back to the Indians, but that doesn't mean we have to give them absolutely everything.'"

"Oh, you don't have to worry about Diana," said Charles. "I know for a fact she's not going to bed with anyone."

"Present company excepted, I assume," replied his uncle.

"No," said Charles.

There was a lengthy pause as Lord Louis contemplated his cheroot.

"Charles," he said, "have you ever wondered why it is that I've not passed on to my just reward?"

"But I thought you had," said Charles.

"Forgive me, my boy, but sitting around talking to you is not my notion of paradise. No, Charles, I'm in a kind of limbo. There's a few of us really — myself, Andy Warhol, the Shah of Iran, a couple of others."

"But why, uncle?"

"Unfinished business. We're not allowed to cross over until our minds are at rest."

"But what unfinished business?" Charles was mystified.

"You," said Lord Louis. "You're my unfinished business."

"Whatever do you mean?"

"Within a few years you'll be king, my boy. I'm not convinced you're ready."

"I think I am."

"A man who is not king in his own home," said Lord Louis, "is hardly ready to be a monarch over millions."

"Not king in my own home?" Charles was miffed. "If I'm not king I'd certainly like to know who is."

"She is."

"Oh." Charles sagged. "You're right of course, uncle, but what am I to do?"

"Stand up to her, my boy. Let her know who's boss."

"I'm afraid she already knows that only too well."

"Until you do," said Lord Louis, "I'm doomed to remain in this damnable state. And I'm tired, Charles. I want to

cross over. I hear it's lovely, much like Henley in the 'twenties."

"I don't know," said Charles, "she's got such an awful temper."

"Release me, Charles." Lord Louis was beginning to fade. "Release me, let me rest."

"Uncle?" cried Charles. But by now all that remained was a smouldering cigar butt.

A h, Philip, there you are." The Queen had begun breakfast without him.

"Mmph," said Philip. It would be a moment or two before he was forming complete sentences.

"Look," said the Queen. "We've had a card from Diana in Canada. 'Having a wretched time, wish I was dead.' There's a picture of Government House on the other side. She's put a little 'x' on their window."

"So they're all right then?" said Philip.

"I shouldn't think so," said the Queen. "So far they've made a right botch of the whole trip but I'm going to let them wriggle out of this mess themselves. What have you got on today, dear?"

"Mmmm, nothing much," said Philip. "Meeting a delegation of former SS officers. Why?"

"I wonder if you'd mind waiting around a bit. Mummy's dropping by. She's got something she wants to tell us. I'm worried about her, Philip. She's been so odd lately."

"Off her nut again, is she?"

"Really, Philip, I wish you'd show a little tact."

"Hello, my dears." It was the Queen Mother, radiant in yellow.

"Hello, Mummy, how well you look today."

"I'm glad you're both here," said the Queen Mother. "I

have wonderful news. I wanted you two to be the first to know. I've decided to re-marry."

The coffee that did not go up Philip's nose sprayed across the carpet.

"Re-marry?" The Queen was aghast. "Don't be ridiculous, Mother, you're eighty-seven!"

"Right you are," the Queen Mother replied, "so there's no time to lose."

"But, Mummy, what would Daddy say?"

"Nothing. He's dead."

"Now see here," said Philip, "who exactly do you plan to marry?"

"Jackie De Silvo."

"Jackie De who?"

"Jackie De Silvo. The entertainer."

"You remember him, Philip," said the Queen. "The last command performance. Some sort of comedian."

"Yes, terribly clever man isn't he?" said the Queen Mother.

Philip had a dim recollection of a weasely fellow with damp hands in a reception line. "Bloody ridiculous, that's what I call it," he said.

"Oh, Mummy," said the Queen, "I don't know what to say."

"You don't have to say a thing. My mind's made up. I've been on my own far too long. I need companionship. Jackie's a dear man. He amuses me."

"Well," said the Queen, "I absolutely forbid this to happen."

"You can forbid many things, dear, but not this. Now, I'm having a little dinner tonight at Clarence House. Mr. De Silvo will be in attendance. I'd like you two to be there as well. I want you to come to know him as the wonderful man he is."

"Don't think I can make it," said Philip. "Pretty sure I've got something on tonight."

"Yes, and I'm afraid I'm rather busy as well," added the Queen.

"Nonsense," said the Queen Mother. "I've checked your calendars and you're both free. Shall we say about eight then?"

At two minutes past one, the red and white Challenger jet touched down at Fredericton and rolled across the tarmac, the royal standard above the cockpit snapping smartly in the breeze. The scream of the engines died to a low whine, the door opened, and Charles and Diana stepped out to be greeted by…no one. There wasn't a soul in sight.

Charles shielded his eyes from the hot light dancing off the concrete. "What's the meaning of this?" he asked the pilot. The flight crew was standing to attention.

"I've no idea, Your Royal Highness." The pilot squirmed. "I can't think what might have happened."

"Oh, this is simply too much!" said Diana. "It's imbecilic!"

"I suppose they did know it was today," said Charles.

"Now what the hell do we do?" asked Diana, plopping down on one of the steps and peeling off her shoes.

The pilot brightened. "If you don't mind me suggesting it, sir, I believe you can get a cab just beyond the terminal."

For the hundredth time the Premier looked at his watch then searched the clear New Brunswick skies. Restless conversation had long since died away and now a great silence hung over the crowd. The welcoming bouquets had begun to wilt.

"For God's sake, more music!" said the Premier and the bandmaster obliged.

Ca-na-
One little, two little, three Canadians
We love you...

It was the fifth time that afternoon the tune had been
trotted out and the Premier thought he might go mad. He
turned to the Lieutenant-Governor. "You'd think," he said,
"that in twenty years someone might have come up with
something else to play." And then, "Say, what's that?"

The Premier pointed skyward to where a distant object
was beginning its descent.

"A bird," said the Lieutenant-Governor. For a moment
they said nothing.

Ca-na-
Five little, six little, seven little provinces...

"I suppose," said the Premier, "they did know it was St.
John."

Charles was doing his best to ease the excitable
Premier towards the door, but the man kept up his
incessant chatter.

"Jeez, I can't tell you how sorry I am," he was saying, "at
least let me get your cab fare. You got the receipt?"

"No, I haven't got the receipt, but it's quite all right.
These things happen." Charles didn't know when, but he
was sure they must.

"I'll get to the bottom of this," the Premier promised.
"Heads will roll!"

"I'm sure they will," said Charles encouragingly.

"Say, where's the princess? I should apologize to her too."
The Premier broke away and headed for a closed door.

"I wouldn't do that if I were you." Charles moved to cut
him off. "Diana's lying down. She's rather tired. As a
matter of fact, I must confess that I'm..."

"Hey, I see you've got one of those little honour-bars." The

Premier was on the move again. "Quite a layout, I must say."

"Yes," Charles agreed. "It's very nice."

"And you've got movies too." The Premier was examining the television. "Look at this, *RoboCop*."

"Please," Charles was almost pleading, "we are rather tired."

"Well jeez, why didn't you just say so? No, don't bother. I'll let myself out. My best to the princess. Tell her not to eat a lot of junk this afternoon. There's a big dinner tonight. A real spread."

"I'll do that," said Charles. "Goodbye." He eased the door shut, then triple locked it and heaved a silent sigh of relief.

"Charles!" He stiffened at the muffled shriek. "Get in here!"

"Coming, darling."

Diana was pretty sure there was something the matter with the Premier. From time to time throughout the dinner, he would slip between the curtains that ran the length of the wall behind the dias. Moments later he would reappear, eyes aglow, talking gibberish. He'd also eaten her dessert.

Now he was on his feet again, addressing the hall, struggling to be heard above the scraping of a thousand plates.

"We have heard the lies," said the Premier, "but now we see the beauty. For with us here tonight, emissaries from a distant world. A lovely Princess Leila" — Diana froze in horror as the Premier brushed her celebrated back — "and a handsome Luke Skywalker." Charles experienced the strange sensation of feeling the Premier's fingers tousling his hair. A lot of people coughed. The Premier turned a page.

"If a tree falls in the forest, and there's no one there to see it, does it make any noise?"

Diana seethed. *Yes*, she thought, *I am an emissary from a distant world. A place called civilization.* Another television apology was in order, she'd decided. One in which each and every Canadian begged her forgiveness. She'd see if Charles could arrange it. Mercifully it seemed that the Premier had meandered towards some sort of conclusion.

"...and so I would ask you to join me now" — he lifted his glass; there was much shuffling of feet — "in a toast to our distinguished visitors, the Prince and Princess of Wales. Through the teeth and over the gums, look out stomach, here she comes."

The Premier drained his glass.

N ow see here, Diana" — Charles's eyes narrowed and his brow creased with firm resolve — "it's time we had a little talk. No, don't try to say anything. For once in your life just listen. It's high time you showed me a little respect. Yes. And when we get home I'll thank you to stop telling Wills that he's going to be king. He's not king until I've been king and I haven't had my turn yet. Yes, it's high time there were some changes made, whether you like it or not. It's time you realized just once and for all just who's in charge ——"

The sudden opening of the door caused Charles to stop in mid-sentence. "Diana!" he said. Diana looked around the room.

"I thought I heard voices."

"Voices?" Oh, must have been me. I was, uh, practising a speech. Yes, a speech I'm going to make, uh, some day. Yes. Must have been that. The voices...you thought you heard. Yes."

"Charles," said Diana.

"Yes, darling?"

"Stop being weird."

Yes, now Philip remembered De Silvo. A little man with rodent features, dressed in a velvet smoking jacket he'd probably lifted from the wardrobe department of the Palladium. Philip glared at him through his wine glass.

"So, De Silvo, you want to marry my mother-in-law?"

"Well, Phil" — De Silvo paused a moment to chew on something — "I'll put it this way. I popped the question and I'll be blowed if Ruffles didn't say yes."

"Who the hell is Ruffles?"

"That's Jackie's pet name for me." The Queen Mother giggled. "Isn't he something?"

"He's something all right." The Queen decided to try a new approach.

"What is your background, Mr. De Silvo?"

"Well now," said De Silvo, "let's see. Butlin's Holiday Camps, I'm a regular there. You probably know that. There's the pantos of course, one or two films. Ever see *Percy's Return?*"

The Queen Mother cut in. "I think she means your family background, Jackie."

"Yes," said Philip. "De Silvo. What's that? Some sort of dago name?"

"I think," said the Queen, "that if we're all through here I suggest, Philip, that you and Jackie go off and get to know each other better. I'll stay here with Mummy."

Philip began his protest. "Well, I don't think that's at all..."

"Yes, come along, Phil," said De Silvo. "I've got some cherry brandy I think might interest you."

Oh, Mummy, how could you?" said the Queen when they were gone.

"You don't care for Mr. De Silvo?"

"We have quite enough idiots in the family without importing more."

"Idiots?" said the Queen Mother. "Oh, you must mean Andrew."

"Yes, and now Diana."

"Diana? What's she done?"

"Oh, nothing much. Just told the Canadians that their country is a ruddy great bore."

The Queen Mother laughed. "Oh, I'm sure the Canadians won't mind. It's like I always say, they're a rough lot but they mean well."

Philip watched with astonishment as De Silvo filled two brandy snifters to the brim.

"Yes, Phil," he was saying, "I'm sure we're going to be the best of friends. And though I do not for a moment dream that I can fill the shoes of Ruffles's ex, his late highness, God bless him, I want to assure you that I will endeavour to be the best of step-fathers to your missus, her majesty."

"All right, De Silvo, how much?"

"I'm sorry," said De Silvo, "I don't understand."

Philip had been sitting. Now he stood. "Let's stop playing about, shall we? How much money will it take to get you out of my mother-in-law's life forever?"

De Silvo clutched his heart. "I must tell you, Phil, I'm shocked."

"Yes, well so was Koo Stark," said Philip, "but we managed to come to an understanding. So what do you say? Five thousand pounds ought to do the job, what?"

De Silvo drew himself up to his full height and glared into Philip's chest. "Five thousand pounds? Do you really think you can destroy my love for that sweet lady with five thousand pounds?" He began to pace the room. "Maybe it's time you learned, Phil, that there are some people even you can't buy. I have proposed to the lady, she has accepted, and I have every intention of honouring my commitment. So keep your five thousand pounds, Phil. I have no need of it."

De Silvo had spoken persuasively and well. It gave Philip pause for thought. "How about ten thousand then?"

"Yes," said De Silvo. "That's much closer to the figure I had in mind."

Yes, Mummy was quite impossible tonight," said the Queen to Philip as the Rolls whisked them through the darkened streets. "I told her that De Silvo man's a bounder. A fortune-hunting bounder."

"You're right, dear," said Philip. He felt more than pleased with himself. "But if I were you I wouldn't be too concerned. Not anymore."

"I told her, Mummy, he's perfectly horrid, but you know how she is when she gets her back up."

"Yes, yes," said Philip impatiently, "but if you'll just listen a moment, dear..."

"So it was hopeless with her. She wouldn't listen."

Like mother, like daughter, thought Philip.

"Don't worry, darling, it's all settled."

"Yes, I know," said the Queen.

"What do you mean you know?"

"Just as we were leaving I took Mr. De Silvo aside and gave him twenty-four hours to clear out of the country."

Philip snorted and answered. "You what?"

"It seemed the only thing left to do."

"I don't believe it! How much did you pay him?"

"Pay him? Why nothing." The Queen thought the question odd.

"Bloody hell!" said Philip.

"But Philip," said the Queen. "I thought you'd be pleased."

Philip was no longer listening. He was rapping on the glass.

"James," he shouted, "turn around!"

"Philip, what on earth are you doing? Where are we going?"

"Back to Clarence House. That bastard's got my ten thousand pounds!"

I t was morning and the Queen had cancelled two engagements to accommodate the unexpected visitor who now stood humbly before her. "You were quite right to come to me regarding this matter, Jessop," she was saying. "As you know, I've had some dealings with Mr. Mollusk in the past."

"I'm so ashamed, Your Majesty. I had no business writing any such book."

"Have you got a copy of your work with you now?" asked the Queen.

Jessop produced his manuscript. The Queen examined the title page.

"'She-Bitch of the Windsors.' How nice. It must be about Diana."

"Yes, Ma'am, and I'm afraid it's none too flattering."

"No," said the Queen. "I don't see how it could be." Jessop sucked in his breath and asked the question he'd dreaded the most. "What do you intend to do about me, Your Majesty? Will I be punished?"

"How long did you work for Diana?" asked the Queen.

"Five years, Your Majesty."

"Then you've been punished enough. We'll consider it time already served."

If Jessop had had a forelock he would have tugged it.

"I am most grateful. But what should I do about Mr. Mollusk? He'll be furious. He's already advanced me twenty thousand pounds and he has my manuscript."

"Let me deal with Mr. Mollusk," said the Queen. She clearly relished the thought. "The twenty thousand pounds we'll consider to be your severance pay. A happy retirement to you, Jessop."

"Thank you, Your Majesty."

"Goodbye, Jessop."

"Goodbye, Your Majesty."

At eleven the Queen notified her staff that she would be unavailable for the remainder of the day. She then settled down to a damn fine read.

D iana coolly surveyed the interior of the Canadian Forces 707. She found it tacky. Charles was at the window staring down on Manitoba or Nova Scotia or wherever the hell they were. Charles was always at the window. There was something odd about him today. He hadn't said a word since take-off.

"Charles," said Diana, "when we get to Calgary I want you to make certain things quite clear. I will not sit through any more long and boring concerts. I will not have objects of any sort thrown in my direction…"

Charles only now became aware that Diana was talking to him.

"…I will not make any more television speeches, I will not be subjected to any more long walks, I will not…"

"Diana," said Charles.

"What?"

"Shut up."

"Charles!"

"'I will not this, I will not that,'" said Charles. "Damn it, Diana, if they want you to light your hair on fire and dance in the nude you'll do it!"

"How dare you!"

"It's time somebody dared. I'm fed up with you. Everyone is fed up with you." Charles stood in the centre aisle of the plane. To Diana he suddenly seemed quite enormous. "The purpose of this trip is business, not pleasure. We're in the business of being royal. We're here to flog some goods, to attract some tourists, and to make old ladies cry for joy. We've got to press the flesh, prop up the politicians, and give the folks a thrill. I've been in this business a lot longer than you and I have every intention of holding on to my job."

"But Charles..."

"But Charles nothing. You've had your own way long enough. When we arrive in Calgary you'll do as you're told. And you'll do it with a smile."

This sudden exertion had left Charles quite drained. He sat down as suddenly as he had stood.

"Charles," said Diana. "I've never heard you speak this way before."

"Well, get used to it," he replied. "I'll be doing a lot more of it in the future."

"I rather hope you do. I mean you seem so, I don't know, different...masterful."

"Do I?" asked Charles. "I mean, I do."

"Yes, you most certainly do."

Diana stared at her husband a long moment.

"Charles."

"Yes?"

"Come here."

"Yes Diana, what do...Oh, Diana! I say!"

Mollusk knew that this time the Queen meant business. This time there'd be no knowing winks, no secret permission to publish. Jessop's memoirs were far too hot for that. This was the showdown. The Queen came right to the point.

"Mr. Mollusk, you are publishing an item this weekend that interests me greatly."

"Ah yes," said Mollusk. "That extraordinary piece on Elvis Presley's brain."

"No, Mr. Mollusk. I think you know exactly which item I mean. The complete works of one A.K. Jessop."

"Oh," said Mollusk. "So you know about that."

"I do and I want it stopped."

Mollusk feigned a sorrowful demeanour. "Ah, regretfully, Your Majesty, I am unable to accommodate you in this matter. I am, of course speaking as a professional journalist."

"And I insist that you do, Mr. Mollusk. I am, of course, speaking as a professional queen."

"Then allow me," said Mollusk, "to point out to you, with all due respect, that there is nothing that you can do to stop me."

As long as Mollusk lived he would never forget what happened next.

The Queen shot Mollusk a withering look. "You think not?" she said. "Mr. Mollusk, you and your paper have been a thorn in my family's side for years. You've completely destroyed what little privacy we have. As my husband has often pointed out, we can't even have a decent whizz in the loo without one of your people sticking his nose in. You've printed distortions, lies…Mr. Mollusk, I've had enough and I'm going to do something about it."

Mollusk was briefly aware of flashing steel. *My God! The woman has gone bloody bonkers! She's wielding a sword!*

"Your Majesty, you can't do this!"

Mollusk's life passed before his eyes. It wasn't a pretty sight.

The Queen raised the sword. Then, it began its descent.

"No!" screamed Mollusk.

"Arise, Sir Rupert," said the Queen.

Mollusk opened his eyes. The sword had come to rest lightly upon his shoulder.

"I beg your pardon?" said Mollusk.

"Arise, Sir Rupert."

"But I don't understand."

"It's perfectly simple. You've been knighted."

Mollusk scrambled to his feet. "My God!" he said, "I don't believe it!"

"Believe it, Sir Rupert," said the Queen. "You are as of this moment a member of the nobility."

It was just now beginning to sink in. "But I...I mean," Mollusk struggled to express his feelings, "I mean, that's bloody marvellous."

"Yes, isn't it?" replied the Queen. "Think of it, Sir Rupert. You have been accorded an honour rarely bestowed, least of all on someone of your profession. Normally, of course, I don't engage in such flamboyance when presenting honours, but I felt sure you would enjoy the cheap theatrics."

"Oh I do," said Mollusk, "I mean, I did."

"And as Sir Rupert," the Queen continued, "you will, of course, be treated with all the respect and dignity due someone of your elevated stature. In short, Sir Rupert, you are one of us."

Mollusk's head swam. "Your Majesty," he said, "how can I ever repay you?"

The Queen looked him up and down. "Oh, there are one or two tasks you might perform."

"Just name them, Your Majesty, and I'll see to it that they're taken care of."

"Well," said the Queen, "since you are so insistent you

might see to it that Jessop's work of fiction is 'taken care of' as you put it."

"Oh now, Your Majesty," said Mollusk, "I'm not sure that…"

"Come, come," said the Queen, "a knight of the realm can't be seen to be the publisher of that sort of trash."

"But, Your Majesty…"

"I remind you," said the Queen, "that you are now one of us, *Sir* Rupert."

Mollusk understood now that he had been bested. He bowed.

"Consider it done, Your Majesty."

"I do," said the Queen. "And while we're on the subject of your newspaper, there are one or two other small improvements I have in mind. Yes, Mr. Mollusk, I believe this could be the beginning of a beautiful…relationship."

Goodbye, goodbye, goodbye to you all, thought Margaret Rose. A farewell for each of you, three envelopes arranged neatly on the table. One for the children — they'd soon forget. One for her sister — she'd never forgive. And one for Mummy. No, that one hadn't gone well at all. But it was done.

A final walk now through the airless rooms where it had taken so long for so little to happen. What would be done with them when she was gone? She realized that she no longer cared.

She closed the door but did not lock it. Then she turned and headed for the garage.

Charles dutifully donned the Indian head-dress. He good-naturedly clambered into a pair of chaps. The souvenir sweatshirt did not quite fit, but he pulled it on all the same. Now he stood at the microphone before a sea of peaked caps. *Mama was right. This is certainly no festival of the arts.*

"...and so it is with great pleasure," said Charles, "that I now declare Yahoo Days officially open."

Somebody yelled "Yahoo." There was the sound of fireworks, or possibly gunshots. Charles returned to his seat.

"Charles," whispered Diana, "I can't do this! It's too dreadful!"

"You'll do it all right," replied Charles, "and you'll do it with a smile."

Diana gripped the reins and tried to settle into the saddle but her mount continued to twist and buck. She was dimly aware of the shouts of encouragement and the rhythmic clapping. The public-address system screeched to life. "And let's give her a big hand, folks! That's the Princess of Wales ridin' the mechanical bull!"

Goodness, thought Diana, *the view from here is magnificent.*

From where she now sat she could just make out the Fowl and Swine exhibit, the shooting gallery, and the Wild Moose ride. And there, just below her, was Charles. He held a baseball in one hand. Now he was winding up, throwing. There was a distant "clang." The crowd roared. Diana shrieked as her perch gave way beneath her. An enormous splash.

"And let's give her a big hand, folks! That's the Princess of Wales floatin' around in there!"

"Oh, Charles, must I?"

"Of course, darling," he replied. "After all, it's for charity."

"But Charles, there are so many of them!"

"Step up, step up." The P.A. system had come to life. "Ten dollars to kiss a real princess!"

"Oh, Charles!"

"Smile, darling."

The first customer laid his money on the line. "Come on, honey, let's have a big wet one!"

Diana closed her eyes and thought of England.

Rain drummed against the palace windows and the dancing light of the fire reflected off panelled walls. The Queen idly stirred her tea.

"You know, Philip," she said, "it's at moments like this that I feel quite content. Charles and Diana are doing well with the Canadians, that horrid Rupert Mollusk has been dealt with."

"Yes," said Philip, "things do seem to have worked out rather well."

"I only wish I could feel better about Mummy," said the Queen.

"She's been so morose since that De Silvo business. Philip, are you listening? What is that you're scribbling at?"

"What dear? Oh. Foreword to a new book, *Fascism: The Reasonable Alternative.*"

"Oh dear," said the Queen.

"Hello, my darlings." It was the Queen Mother, indelible in indigo.

"Mummy!" said the Queen. "We were just talking about you."

"How are you then?" said Philip. "Still moping about that greaseball De Silvo?"

"Philip!" said the Queen.

"Oh you needn't worry about me." The Queen Mother

was radiant. "I'm all over that now. I realize he was a most unsuitable choice."

"I'm so glad, Mummy," said the Queen. "Now my mind is truly at rest."

"Yes," the Queen Mother went on, "I was blinded by my passion. You won't catch me making the same mistake again."

"I'm so relieved," said the Queen.

"And I can tell you that Mr. De Silvo couldn't begin to hold a candle to my new fiancé."

"Your what?" Philip wasn't sure he'd heard right.

"Now really, Mummy!" said the Queen.

"Hear me out," said the Queen Mother. "He's a wonderful man, courtly and charming. He has a diplomatic background, you may know him already. He has a small encumbrance, a wife, but he'll soon be rid of her, he assures me. He's just outside, judge for yourselves."

"Oh this is too much," said the Queen.

The Queen Mother opened the door. "Come in, my love, come in."

There was something immediately familiar about the distinguished greying man who entered. Something familiar and utterly disturbing. It dawned on Philip first.

"Bloody hell! Why you're, you're…"

Now the Queen had the same awful realization. "Oh, Mummy," she said, "how could you?"

But it was too late to stop the Queen Mother now.

"Everyone say hello to Mr. Kurt Waldheim!"

Princess Margaret Rose made sure the garage door was shut tight. She wanted to do this right. It must be neat. It must be quick. She removed her clothes. In a few moments she would start the motor and it would be all over. The leather outfit was just where she had left it.

There was a mechanical quality to her movements as she put it on.

It's as if I'm watching myself do this, she thought. *Where is the Sony Walkman? Ah, there it is.* She wanted music when she went.

She started the motor. A shattering roar filled the garage. A single headlight pierced the gloom. Margaret clapped on the earphones and cranked up Steppenwolf.

Get your motor running,
Head out on the highway,
Lookin' for adventure,
Or whatever comes my way...

Finally the helmet. Margaret Rose mounted the Norton Commando. Now she would begin to live. She flicked a switch and doors rolled obediently open. A couple of satisfying revs and the Norton shot forward, up the ramp and into the night. She was last seen heading south on Kensington Church Street and pulling a left at the High Street. France was mere hours away.

Sometime during the night that knowledge snatched from us at birth was restored to him. A sudden rush of understanding electrified his mind and forced him bolt upright with a startled, "Of course, it's all so simple!" He looked about. It was dawn. He had never seen such light.

They came for him within the hour and guided him with firm deference to the outskirts of the city. At noon a shimmering fanfare, the result of a collaboration between Benjamin Britten, William Walton, and Franz Joseph Haydn. The salute of twenty-one cannon reverberated among the golden spires. An enormous crowd had begun to gather in the great plaza. He could make out the faces of several — General Slim and crazy Orde Wingate, even cousin Anastasia. And, by George, there was Edwina, more beautiful than ever. He was about to wave and call out when he noticed the figure next to her and stopped himself. *Who is that with his arm around her waist? Why it's…* he could scarcely believe it. *Damn that Nehru!*

But now the great gates were beginning to swing open. A shower of bells peeled through the crystal air. And at 12:03 precisely, Lord Louis Mountbatten, dressed in the uniform of a First Sea Lord, entered into the Kingdom of Heaven.

THE
ROYAL HOUSE
OF WINDSOR

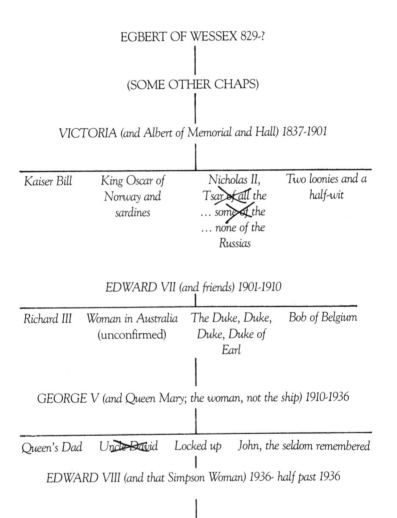

EGBERT OF WESSEX 829-?

|

(SOME OTHER CHAPS)

|

VICTORIA (and Albert of Memorial and Hall) 1837-1901

|

| Kaiser Bill | King Oscar of Norway and sardines | Nicholas II, Tsar of all the ... some of the ... none of the Russias | Two loonies and a half-wit |

EDWARD VII (and friends) 1901-1910

| Richard III | Woman in Australia (unconfirmed) | The Duke, Duke, Duke, Duke of Earl | Bob of Belgium |

|

GEORGE V (and Queen Mary; the woman, not the ship) 1910-1936

|

| Queen's Dad | Uncle David | Locked up | John, the seldom remembered |

EDWARD VIII (and that Simpson Woman) 1936- half past 1936

|

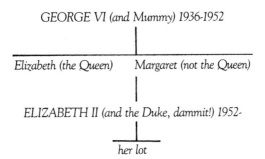

GEORGE VI (and Mummy) 1936-1952

Elizabeth (the Queen)　　　Margaret (not the Queen)

ELIZABETH II (and the Duke, dammit!) 1952-

her lot

THE ORDER
OF SUCCESSION
TO THE THRONE

Prince Charles
Prince William
Prince Henry
Prince Andrew
Prince Edward
Princess Anne
Princess Margaret
Viscount Linley
Lady Sarah Armstrong-Jones
Barbara Cartland
Hector Barrantes
Rula Lenska
Dame Edna Everidge
Joan Collins
A Mad Cousin
Princess Diana
Alistair Cooke
Cliff Richards
Sir Robin Day
A Man in Texas
David Frost
Boy George
The Scugwells
You.

Paul K. Willis is a Toronto based writer and broadcaster. For some years he was the taller half of the comedy duo, La Troupe Grotesque. In its colourful history La Troupe graced the stages of the National Arts Centre, New York's Catch A Rising Star, and once, by mistake, the Choo-Choo Stop in Guelph.

His comedy has been heard on CBC Radio's "Sunday Morning," "As It Happens," "The Entertainers," and "Prime Time," and on television's "The Journal."

Most recently he wrote the radio comedy specials: "This Hour Has Seventeen Programs," "The Year Of Living Obnoxiously," and "If You Love This Government." All were nominated for ACTRA awards. Mr. Willis stumbled home from these events haggard and empty handed.

In his spare time Mr. Willis campaigns tirelessly for world peace and takes in homeless kittens.